Snow Happy to be Here!

the Slightly Silly Story of the Snowblatt Family

Hallmark

Snow Happy to be Here!
The Slightly Silly Story of the Snowblatt Family

Editorial Director: Todd Hafer
Editor: Jeff Morgan
Art Director: Kevin Swanson
Designer: Michelle Nicolier
Production Artist: Dan Horton

Printed and bound in China.
ISBN: 978-1-59530-175-8
First Edition, March 2007
10 9 8 7 6 5 4 3 2 1
1LPR7085

One day the Snowblatts were having a chat,
as they do when the humans aren't near,
when suddenly little Snow-Ellen piped up
and said in a voice crystal clear—

Papa

Snow-Ellen

"Where do we come from, and why were we made,
and how did we get here from there?"
"Yeah," joined in Snow-John, "I want to know, too.
Did we—POOF!—just appear from thin air?"

Mama

Snow-John

Mama and Papa just winked at each other.
"Good question!" said Mama. "Let's see,
maybe it's time that I tell you the tale
of how snowpeople all come to be.

"It starts with the snowflakes that fly from the sky
to wherever on earth they are blown—
zillions of snowflakes, but each one unique
with a destiny all of its own.

"Some will be snowballs, and some will be forts,
and some will melt down to the sea.
Some will be skied on, and some will be slid on,
and some will become you and me!"

"But how do these snowflakes get made into us?"
said the snowkids with some consternation.
"I'll answer that," replied Papa Snowblatt—
"It's location, location, LOCATION!"

"What Papa is saying," continued his wife,

"is that snowflakes are only the start.

There have to be fun-loving humans nearby,

because they do the magical part.

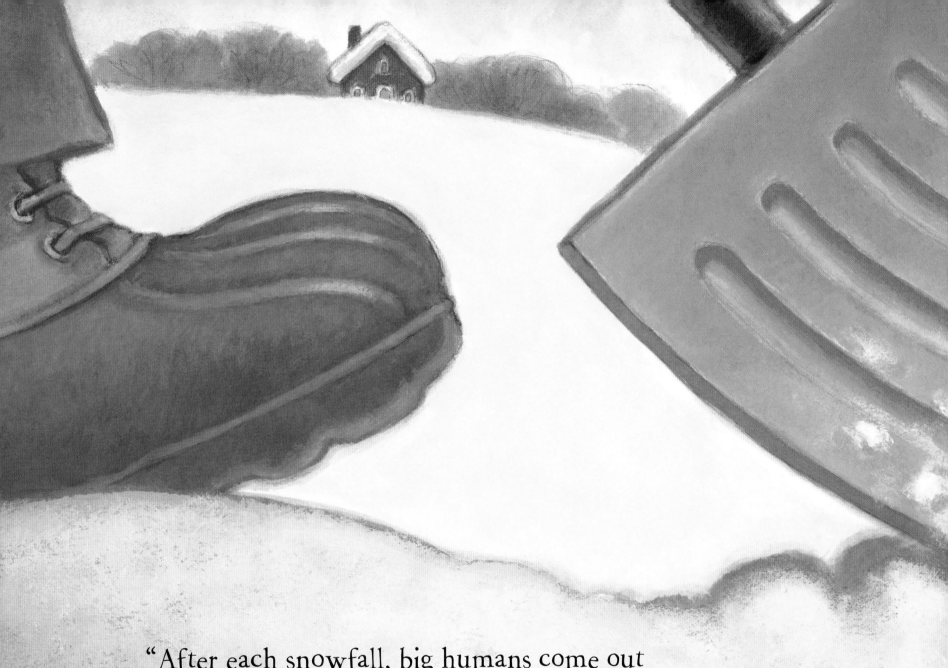

"After each snowfall, big humans come out
and start sweeping and shoveling and stomping.
Then small humans appear dressed in silly snow gear
and go running and romping and clomping.

"Sooner or later, they get the idea
to begin rolling balls of all sizes—
some giant, some tiny, some lumpy, some shiny.
And, of course, there are always surprises!

"When they start attacking the issue of stacking,

they find that it's not very easy.

There's huffing and puffing and wobbling and bobbling

that leave the poor things kind of wheezy.

Stinky

Ms. Natural

"Then comes the part where we get all our features—
our eyes, ears, and noses, and such.

Sugar

Slick

Capt. Icebuckle

Capt. Icebuckle

Trooper

"As you may have noticed, materials vary,
so we each get that personal touch."

Fifi

Tooley

"Yeah, that's for sure," Snow-John said with a grin.
"You know we all look kind of weird.
Plus, none of us match each other at all,
and just think about Grandpapa's beard!"

"That's right," said Snow-Ellen, "and how about clothes?
Have you ever seen such funny stuff?"

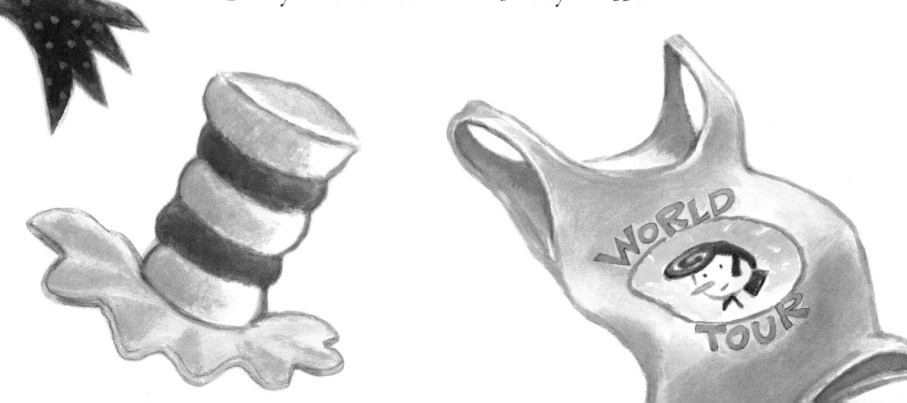

"Hey, wait there a minute," said Papa Snowblatt,
"you're focusing on the mere fluff."

"I agree," added Mama. "You're missing the point.

It's a miracle we're even here.

Our humans may not have the best taste in fashion,

but they know what they're doing, that's clear.

"After they've rolled us and buttoned and bowed us
and patted down each little flake,
they step back with pride, and then they provide
what we need to be finally awake."

"What is it? What is it?" exclaimed the snowkids.

"Is it hard? Does it take a long while?"

"No," explained Mama, "it just takes a moment—
they bring us to life when they smile."

We'd love to hear from you
if you have enjoyed this book.

PLEASE SEND YOUR COMMENTS TO:

Book Feedback

Hallmark Cards,Inc.

Mail Drop 215

2501 McGee,

Kansas City, MO 64108

or e-mail us at

booknotes@hallmark.com